# Speech Rhymes

*chosen by*
## CLIVE SANSOM

A. & C. BLACK LTD. LONDON

*In this same series*
Acting Rhymes
Counting Rhymes
Rhythm Rhymes
*Also by Clive Sansom*
Speech and Communication in the Primary School (Black)

First published in one volume 1974
Reprinted 1975, 1976, 1977
© 1974 A. & C. Black Ltd 35 Bedford Row WC1R 4JH
ISBN 0 7136 1425 0
Printed and bound in Great Britain by
TINDAL PRESS LIMITED
Chelmsford Essex

# CONTENTS

# INTRODUCTION

If a child is to express himself successfully in all situations, whether in daily living or in such activities as creative drama, he needs assistance in controlling his voice and developing his speech. The rhymes in this book provide practice material similar to the exercises and studies which teach control in music, so helping the child to speak easily and naturally in a variety of situations.

The rhymes are meant to be spoken aloud. They are lively, enjoyable, amusing, and call for a wide variety of expression.

Teachers using them as part of a speech training programme will find explanatory notes at the end of the book. The rhymes are divided into three sections in order of difficulty.

## PART 1

## Dandelion Clocks

wh——wh——wh——wh—
One o'clock, two o'clock, three o'clock,
     four—
I found a fairy clock close to my door.

wh——wh——wh——wh—
Five o'clock, six o'clock, seven o'clock,
     eight—
I blew and I blew, and I found it was
     late.

wh——wh——wh——wh—
I blew and I blew till I counted to ten—
And now I'm beginning all over again!

wh——wh——WH!

*J. E. Mulliner*

# The Busy Bee

Bùzz, buzz, bùzz, went the bùsy little
     bèe,
Bùzz, buzz, bùzz, buzz, bùzz went hè.
"What is your name, you busy little
     bee?"
—"Buzz, buzz, buzz, buzz, *buzz*!"
     said he.

*Evelyn Abraham*

# Robin Redbreast

Little Robin Redbreast
    Sat upon a rail;
Niddle-noddle went his head,
    And wag went his tail.

Niddle-noddle went his head,
    And wag went his tail,
As little Robin Redbreast
    Sat upon a rail.

*Traditional*

# Guessing Game

1   Guess what is making the sound you
        hear:

     zzz——zzz——zzz.

2   A bee is making the sound I hear,

     zzz——zzz——zzz.


3   Guess what is making the sound you
        hear:

     sh——sh——sh.

4   The sea is making the sound I hear,

     sh——sh——sh.

     *(Now go on)*

# Moo-Cow

"Moo-cow, Moo-cow,
How do you do, cow?"

"Very well, thank you—
Moo, moo, moo."

*W. Kingdon-Ward*

# Motoring

My motor is humming,
I'm coming, I'm coming,
Make room, make room, make room!
Not a minute to wait,
I'm late, I'm late,
Make room, make room, make room!

*Mona Swann*

# Miss Mouse

There was a little mouse
Who had a little house,
And a very proud mouse was she,
For it had a little door
Quite close to the floor
And as round as a door could be.

There came a fat rat,
Who went *rat-tat*
On the little round door in the wall.
"Will you let me in?
I'm very very thin,
And I'll be no trouble at all."

"You're *not* very thin,
And I *won't* let you in,"
Said little Miss Mouse inside.
"You're very very stout,
I should never get you out,
So find somewhere else to hide!"

She shut her little door
More tight than before,
And that is THE END because
That's all about the house
And the funny little mouse
And the proud little mouse that she was.

*Clive Sansom*


## Sheep and Lambs

"Maa!" say the lambs,
"Baa!" say their mothers.
"So that's where you are!
Have you been far?"
"Ah!" say the lambs.
"Baa!" say their mothers.

*Rodney Bennett*

# The Aeroplane

The plane is travelling up in the sky,
   vvv——vvv——vvv,
Moving so fast, and ever so high,
   vvv——vvv——vvv.

Over the land, and over the sea,
   vvv——vvv——vvv,
But we always come back in time for tea,
   vvv——vvv——vvv.

# Buttons

Buttons, buttons,
I can do up buttons!
I do all my buttons up
When I go to town.
For I have six buttons,
Big round buttons,
Six buttons on my coat
All coloured brown!

*W. Kingdon-Ward*

# Toys

Toys! Toys! Toys!
Who'll buy my toys?
Some for girls, some for boys,
Toys! Toys! Toys!

*Agnes Curren Hamm*

# The Rain

1

Pitter-patter,
Pitter-patter,
Listen to the rain!
Pitter-patter,
Pitter-patter,
On the window pane!

*W. Kingdon-Ward*

2

Rain on the house-top,
Rain on the tree,
Rain on the green grass—
But don't rain on me!

*Traditional*

# Ringing the Bell

Ring the bell!    Ting-a-ling-ling!
Knock at the door!    Rat-tat-tat!
Draw the latch!    Click-clack!
AND WALK RIGHT IN

# Wishing

If I were a bell,
I would go a-ringing;
If I were a bird,
I would go a-singing;

If I were a fairy,
I would go a-dancing;
If I were a horse,
I would go a-prancing.

But I'm none of these,
So it's no use wishing.
John's come home,
And we're both going fishing.

*Peggy Noble*

# Marching

Màrching in our Wèllingtons,
    Tràmp, tramp, tràmp,
Marching in our Wellingtons,
    We wòn't get dàmp.

Splashing through the puddles
    In the rain, rain, rain—
Splashing through the puddles,
    And splashing home again!

*Clive Sansom*

# Nancy Brittle

    Nancy Brittle
    Bought a kettle,
Put it on the hob.
    Nancy Brittle
    Burned the kettle.
Sob! Sob! Sob!

*Ruth Large*

# Singing Time

I wake in the morning early,
And always the very first thing,
I sit up in bed and I poke out my head,
And I sing, and I sing, and I sing!

*Rose Fyleman*


# The Steam-Train
# and the Hill

I wish I could,
    I wish I could,
        I wish I could.

I think I can,
    I think I can,
        I think I can.

I thought I could,
    I thought I could,
        I thought I could . . .

# Going to Sea

"Hullo, sailor!"
   "Hullo, man!"
"Bring me a coconut!"
   "Yes, if I can;

I'll bring you a sword
   And a silken fan!"
"Good-bye, sailor!"
   "Good-bye, man!"

*Clive Sansom*

# Haircut

The barber's clippers went clip, clip,
      clip,
And his snippers went snip, snip, snip.
Clip went the clippers; snip went the
      snippers;
Clip, clip; snip, snip, snip!

*Evelyn Abraham*

# Listening

I hear a bee, humming near a flower:
    m-m-m; m-m-m.
I hear a clock striking out the hour:
    Ding-dong, Ding-dong.

I hear the spinning of a big red top:
    n-n-n; n-n-n.
Keep them all going—don't let them
      stop!
    m-m; Ding-dong; n-n;
    m-m; Ding-dong; n-n.

*Agnes Curren Hamm*


# Three Kittens

Three little kittens
Had six little mittens
For three little pairs of hands;

But how little kittens
Can put on their mittens
*No*body understands!

*Clive Sansom*

# Jack Sprat's Pig

Little Jack Sprat
   Once had a pig.
It was not very little,
   It was not very big;
It was not very lean,
   It was not very fat.
"It's a good pig to grunt!"
   Said little Jack Sprat.

*Traditional*

# Rat-a-Tat-Tat

Rat-a-tat-tat!
Who is that?
Only grandma's pussy-cat.
What do you want?
A pint of milk.
Where is your money?
In my pocket.
Where is your pocket?
I forgot it.
Oh, you silly pussy-cat!

*London Street Game*

# The Greedy Jackdaw

"Caw", said the Jackdaw,
　"Caw! . . . Caw!"
—What is he calling for?
　"More, more, more!"

# Ducky-Daddles

Ducky-Daddles
Loves the puddles.
How he waddles
As he paddles
In the puddles—
Ducky-Daddles!

*W. Kingdon-Ward*

# Mice

Mice . . . mice,
Eating up the rice.
"Nibble-nibble, nibble-nibble,
Nice, nice, nice!"

*S. K. Vickery*

# What are you?

I am a gold lock;
I am a gold key.

I am a silver lock;
I am a silver key.

I am a brass lock;
I am a brass key.

I am a lead lock;
I am a lead key.

I am a monk lock;
I am a mon -key.

*Catch-rhyme*

# The Spider

I saw a spider
Crawl—crawl—crawl.
I saw a spider
Crawling up the wall.

*W. Kingdon-Ward*

# The Candle

Where does the flame on the candle go
When you blow it out? I would like to
know.
Where does it come from?
Where does it go?
That is what I would like to know.

*Peggy Noble*

# Sing a Song

Sing a song of buttercups,
Filled with golden sun;
Sing a song of daisy flowers—
Summertime's begun!

Sing a song of singing birds,
Singing all for fun;
Sing a song of summertime—
Summertime's begun.

# Moppety-Moppit

Moppety-Moppit
And Poppety-Pop
Went on their way
With a skip and a hop—
One with a skip,
One with a hop,
Moppety-Moppit
And Poppety-Pop!

*W. Kingdon-Ward*

# Pease Pudding

Pease pudding hot,
　Pease pudding cold,
Pease pudding in the pot,
　Nine days old.

Some like it hot,
　Some like it cold,
Some like it in the pot
　Nine days old.

*Warwickshire Folk-rhyme*

# Bottles of Water

Water in bottles,
    Water in pans,
Water in kettles,
    Water in cans—
It is always the shape
    Of whatever it's in,
Bucket or kettle,
    Or bottle or tin.

*Rodney Bennett*

# What is it?

There was a little green house,
And in the little green house
There was a little brown house,
And in the little brown house
There was a little yellow house,
And in the little yellow house
There was a little white house,
And in the little white house
There was a little heart.

# The Foolish Man

I knew a man who always wore
A saucepan on his head.
I asked him what he did it for—
"I don't know why", he said.
"It always makes my ears so sore;
I am a foolish man.
I should have left it off before
And worn a frying-pan."

*Christopher Chamberlain*

# Four Happy Hens

1 "I've laid an ègg, chook-chòok!"
2 —"I've laid an ègg, chook-chòok!"
3 —"And anòther one, chòok!"
4 —"And anòther one, chòok!"
ALL   Now whàt do you thìnk
      Of *thàt*, chook-chòok?

*Ruth Large*

# Which Pig was Which?

A long-tailed pig, or a short-tailed pig,
    Or a pig without any tail?
A sow-pig or a boar-pig
    Or a pig with a curly tail?

# Washing Linen

We are washing linen, linen,
We are washing linen clean.

We are rinsing linen, linen,
We are rinsing linen clean.

We are wringing linen, linen,
We are wringing linen clean.

We are hanging linen, linen,
We are hanging linen clean.

We are wearing linen, linen,
We are wearing linen clean.

*London Street Game*

# Bibblibonty

On the Bibblibonty hill
Stands a Bibblibonty house;
In the Bibblibonty house
Are Bibblibonty people;
The Bibblibonty people
Have Bibblibonty children;
And the Bibblibonty children
Take a Bibblibonty sup
With a Bibblibonty spoon
From a Bibblibonty cup.

*Translated from the Dutch*
*by Rose Fyleman*

# Threads and Thimbles

"My thread is too thick!"
"My thread is too thin!"
"So this is the thing we'll do.
We both will ask Mother
To give us another,
And with it a thimble, too."

*Mona Swann*

# Follow my Leader

Fòllow-my-leader, fòllow-my-leader,
Fòllow-my-leader àfter me.
Fòllow me up to the tòp of the hill,
And fòllow me down to the sèa.

*Clive Sansom*


# If I had Plenty of Money

If only I had plenty of money
I'd buy you some flowers, and I'd buy
    you some honey,
I'd buy you a boat, and I'd buy you a
    sail,
I'd buy you a cat with a long bushy tail,
I'd buy you a brooch and a bangle as
    well,
I'd buy you a church, and I'd buy you
    the bell,
I'd buy you the earth, I'd buy you the
    moon—
Oh, money, dear money, please come
    very soon!

*Paul Edmonds*

# The Rabbit

Rabbit in the hollow
Sits and sleeps;
Hunter in the forest
Nearer creeps.

Little rabbit, have a care,
Sleeping in the hollow there!
Quickly, little rabbit,
You must run, run, run!

*Australian Song-Game*

# The President's Tea

O Pillykin, Willykin, Winky, Wee,
How does the President take his tea?
He takes it with melons, he takes it with
    milk,
He takes it with syrup and sassafras silk★;
He takes it without, he takes it within—
O Punky-doodle and Jollapin!

*American Rhyme*

★A liquid from the bark of the sassafras tree

# The Windmill

Blòw, wind, blòw!
And gò, sails, gò!
That the mìller may grind his còrn;
That the baker may take it,
    and into rolls make it,
And sènd us some hot in the mòrn.

*Traditional*

# Ducks

Sèe the little dùcks come wàddling down
    the làne,
  Wàddle-waddle-quàck! wàddle-waddle-
    quàck!
Marching in the mud and paddling in the
    rain,
  Waddle-waddle-quack! waddle-waddle-
    quack!
"We're gòing to the pònd and we're nèver
    coming bàck again,
  Wàddle-waddle, quàck-quack-quàck!"

*Clive Sansom*

# Look Out!

Look out! Look out!
   A motor is coming!
Look out! Look out!
   A motor is coming!
    LOOK OUT!

Here it comes splashing
And hooting and dashing,
Look out, look out, look out!

Look out! Look out!
   A motor is coming!
Look out! Look out!
   A motor is coming!
    LOOK OUT!

*Paul Edmonds*

# Out Goes – Who?

Inty, tinty, tethery, methery,
Bank for over, Dover, ding.

*Counting-Out Rhyme*

# The Grasshopper

Grasshopper, grasshopper, draw your
　　bow,
　　Whirrekee, whirrekee, whirroo;
Play us a tune before we go,
　　Whirrekee, whirrekee, whirroo.
Here, where the grasses grow long and
　　rank,
　　Whirrekee, whirrekee, whirroo,
Over the slopes of the moonlit bank,
　　Whirrekee, whirrekee, whirroo,
Under the light of the yellow moon,
　　Whirrekee, whirrekee, whirroo—
Grasshopper, play us your beautiful
　　tune,
　　Whirrekee, whirrekee, whirroo.

*W. Kingdon-Ward*

# Silly Billy

"Silly Billy! Silly Billy!"
　—"Why is Billy silly?"
"Silly Billy hid a shilling;
　Isn't Billy silly?"

*Mona Swann*

# Riding in the Rain

The rain comes pittering, pattering down,
    Plipperty, plipperty, plop!
The farmer drives his horse to town,
    Clipperty, clipperty, clop!
The rain comes pattering,
Horse goes clattering,
    Clipperty, plipperty, plop!

# Hoppety's House

Here is a little house
High on a hill,
Hippety high,
Hippety hill,
With Hoppety hurrying
Home with a will,
Home to his house on the hill.
Hoppety hurrying,
Hippety home,
Hurrying home to his house on the hill.

*Rodney Bennett*

# Jeremiah

Jeremiah, blow the fire,
    Puff, puff, puff!
First you blow it gently,
    Then you blow it rough.
    wh! WH!


# North Wind and South Wind

If the smoke from the mouth
Of the chimney goes south,
It's the North wind that blows
From the country of snows.
Look out for rough weather—
The cold and the North wind
Come always together.

If the smoke pouring forth
From the chimney goes north,
A mild day it will be,
A warm time we shall see.
The South wind is blowing
From lands where the orange
And fig trees are growing.

# Goose Girl

Goose Girl! Goose Girl!
  Come and mind your geese.
They're making such a cackling,
  We don't get any peace.
Lead them to the water,
  Where they want to be,
And sit you down to watch them
  Beneath the willow tree.

*Irene Pawsey*


# Misty Moisty

Misty moisty was the morn,
  Chilly was the weather;
There I met an old man
  Dressed all in leather—

Dressed all in leather
  Against the wind and rain,
With "How do you do?" and "How do
    you do?"
  And "How do you do?" again.

*Traditional*

## PART 2

## The Bus Conductor

All day long
You'll hear him sing:
"Tickets, please! Tickets!
Ting——ting-a-ling!

Next stop the palace,
Who's for the king?
Pass along quickly!
Ting-a-ling, ting!"

Summer and winter,
Autumn and spring,
He hurries along
With his ting——ting-a-ling!

With his ting——ting-a-ling!
And his ting-a-ling, ting!
"Tickets, please! Tickets!
Ting——ting-a-ling!"

*Clive Sansom*

# London Town

1   Which is the way to London Town
     To see the king in his golden crown?

2   One foot up, and one foot down—
     That's the way to London Town.

1   Which is the way to London Town
     To see the queen in her silken gown?

2   Left!—right! Up and down—
     Soon you'll be in London Town.

*Traditional*

# I Have a Little Cough, Sir

I have a little cough, sir,
In my little chest, sir.
Every time I cough, sir,
It leaves a little pain, sir,
Cough, cough, cough, cough,
There it is again, sir.

*Robert Graves*

35

# Echo

| *Caller :* | *Echo :* |
|---|---|
| Hi! | Hi! |
| Can you hear me? | . . . hear me? |
| Are you near me? | . . . near me? |
| Hi! | Hi! |

# Dance, Dot; Dance, Dan

Dance, Dot; dance, Dan,
   Dance, dance, do.
Down the dale and down the dell
   I'll dance too.

*Rodney Bennett*

# The Clock

Tick-tack, tick-tock,
   Tell the time true.
Tick-tack, tick-tock,
   Ten past two.

*Mona Swann*

# Wishing

If I'd as much money as I could spend,
I never would cry, "Old chairs to mend,
Old chairs to mend, Old chairs to mend."
I never would cry, "Old chairs to mend."

If I'd as much money as I could tell,★
I never would cry, "Old clothes to sell,
Old clothes to sell, Old clothes to sell."
I never would cry, "Old clothes to sell."

★count                                    *Old Song*

# Lily Lee

I like Lily,
Little Lily Lee;
I like Lily
And Lily likes me.
Lily likes lollipops,
Lemonade and lime-drops,
But I like Lily,
Little Lily Lee.

*Isobel Best*

# The Kangaroo

Old Jumpety-Bumpety-Hop-and-Go-
    One
Was lying asleep on his side in the sun.
This old kangaroo, he was whisking
    the flies
(With his long glossy tail) from his ears
    and his eyes.
Jumpety-Bumpety-Hop-and-Go-One
Was lying asleep on his side in the sun,
Jumpety-Bumpety-Hop!

*Australian Song-Game*


# The Crow

Says the crow in the cornfield:
    "Caw, caw, caw."
He's a very bold robber—
    He fears no law,
Nor yet the tall scarecrow,
    And really he ought,
For some day this robber
    Is sure to be caught.

# The Cobbler

Walking through the town one day,
I peeped in a window over the way;
And putting his needle through and
    through,
There sat the cobbler making a shoe.
For the world he cares never the whisk
    of a broom—
All he wants is elbow-room.
      Rap-a-tap-tap, tick-a-tack-too,
      That is the way to make a shoe!

*From an old rhyme*


# Tea-time for Timothy

Tell little Timothy
    it's nearly time for tea;
The ticker on the mantelpiece
    says half-past-three.
If he wants some tea today
    he'd better come and see.
There are strawberry-tarts for Timothy
    and buttered toast for me.

*Clive Sansom*

# Flying Kites

Our kites are flying high in the sky,
  High in the sky, high in the sky,
Our kites are flying high in the sky—
  Tiny and white like a butterfly.

Higher and higher still they climb,
  Still they climb, still they climb,
Higher and higher still they climb—
  Oh, it's fine flying kites in
    summertime!


# The King's High Drummer

He was Bang-bang-banging on his
Big Bass Drum,
And the Regiment went marching to his
Thr-r-rum-thrum-thrum.
They came marching up the garden
    with their
Firm hard tread,
A line of British soldiers with a
Drummer at their head.

*Caryl Brahms*

# Chitterabob

There was a man, and his name was
    Dob,
And he had a wife, and her name was
    Mob,
And he had a dog, and he called it Cob,
And she had a cat called Chitterabob.

    "Cob", says Dob,
    "Chitterabob", says Mob.
    Cob was Dob's dog,
    Chitterabob Mob's cat.

*Traditional*


# Bird-scaring Rhyme

Shoo! all you birds,
Shoo! all you birds.
I'll up with my clappers,
And knock you down backwards.
Shoo! all you birds,
    Shoo!

*Gloucestershire Folk-rhyme*

# The Cow Says . . . .

The còw says "Mòo"; the dòve says
    "Còo";
And the ròoster on the òld grey
    fòwlhouse ròof
Says "Còck-a-doodle, dòodle-doodle,
    dòodle-doodle-dòo!"

*Evelyn Abraham*

# Little Pony

Clippety-clap,
What a fine little chap,
Clippety-clippety-clap.
He goes click-clack
With his feet on the track—
Oh, how I'd like to be
Riding his back
Going——
    Clippety, clippety,
    Clippety, clippety,
    Clippety, clippety, clap!

*Clive Sansom*

# The Huntsmen

Three jolly gentlemen,
    In coats of red,
Rode their horses
    Up to bed.

Three jolly gentlemen
    Snored till morn,
Their horses champing
    The golden corn.

Three jolly gentlemen,
    At break of day,
Came clitter-clatter down the stairs
    And galloped away.

*Walter de la Mare*


# Ned

Ned, Ned,
The donkey's dead!
He died last night
With a pain in his head.

*Warwickshire Folk-rhyme*

43

# A Strange Tale

"Did you ever, ever, ever
In your life, did you ever
See a whale catch a snail by the tail?"

"No, I never, never, never
In my life, no, I never
Saw a snail's tail caught by a whale."

# The Cold Old House

I know a house, and a cold old house,
   A cold old house by the sea.
If I were a mouse in that cold old house
   What a cold cold mouse I'd be!

# The Pieman

As I was going down Mincing Lane,
Mincing Lane on a Christmas Day,
"Hot mince pies!", a pieman cries,
"Two for a penny, and look at the size!"

# Pelican Chorus

Wing to wing we dance around,
Stamping our feet with a flumpy sound,
Opening our mouths as pelicans ought—
And this is the song we nightly snort:

    Ploffskin, Pluffskin, Pelican jee!
    We think no birds so happy as we!
    Plumpskin, Ploshskin, Pelican jill!
    We think so then, and we thought
        so still.

*Edward Lear*


# Hoppety

Hoppety the Kangaroo
Goes hurrying along.
His hind-legs help him when he hops,
His tail is thick and strong.
The trouble is that once he starts
He finds it hard to stop—
Hop, hop, hoppety,
Hop, hop, hop!

*Clive Sansom*

# The Town Crier

Oyez!* Oyez!
There's a fair today!
Come, win a prize
At the coconut shies!
There are hooplas and swings,
And many such things
At the fair today—
Oyez! Oyez!

*Pronounced *Oh-yay* (Listen)

# Bells and Birds

Ding-dong! Ding-dong!
All the bells are ringing.
Ding-dong! Ding-dong!
Ringing all the day.

Sing-song! Sing-song!
All the birds are singing.
Sing-song! Sing-song!
Let's go out and play.

# Pancake

Mix a pancake,
Stir a pancake,
   Pop it in the pan.
Fry the pancake,
Toss the pancake,
   Catch it if you can.

*Christina Rossetti*

# Plain Jane

"Pudding and pie,"
Said Jane—"Oh my!"

"Which would you rather?"
Asked her father.

"Both!" said Jane,
Quite bold and plain.

# As I was going along

As I was going along, long, long,
A-singing a comical song, song, song,
The lane that I went was so long,
    long, long,
And the song that I sang was so long,
    long, long,
That the words and the music went
    wrong, wrong, wrong,
As I went singing along!

# Woodpecker

Tip-tap, tip-tap,
Tip-a-tap-tee,
Tip-tapping woodpecker
Taps on a tree.
Tapping from the tip-top,
Tip-taps he,
Right down the trunk
Of the tired old tree.

*Isobel Best*

# The Airman

rrrrrrrrrrr

The engine roars,
The propeller spins,
"Close the doors!"
Our flight begins.


zzzzzzzzzzzz

The plane rises;
It skims the trees.
Over the houses
We fly at our ease.


mmmmmm

ZOOM goes the plane,
The engine hums.
Then home again,
And down it comes . . .


mmmm m m
z z zmmmmm m m
z z z
z z zzzzrrrrrrrrrrrrrrrrrrrrrr

*Clive Sansom*

# Our Bicycle

This is the way we pump the tyre:
    ffffffffffff       ffffffffffff.
See it get higher and higher and higher:
    ffffffffffff       ffffffffffff.

Punctures make the cycle slower:
    ffffffffffffffffff.
See it get lower and lower and lower:
    ffffffffffffffffffffff.

*Clive Sansom*


# Washing-Day

I rub and I rub
At the tub, tub, tub,
The clothes in the suds to scrub, scrub,
    scrub;
But when they are clean,
And white to be seen,
I'll dress like a lady, and dance on the
    green.

# Rain

Rain, rain, rain, rain, rain, rain, rain,
Go away, rain, go away!
We don't want you every day.

Rain, rain, rain, rain, rain, rain, rain,
Go away, go away, go away!
Go away, rain, go away!

Rain, rain, rain, rain, rain, rain, rain,
Go away, rain, go away!
For we can't go out and play
When it rains all day,
Go away, rain, go away!

*Paul Edmonds*

# The Clothes Line

Hand in hand they dance in a row,
Hither and thither, to and fro.
Flip, flap, flop, and away they go—
Fluttering creatures as white as snow.

# Marching

1   *The Grand Old Duke*

Oh, the grànd old Dùke of Yòrk,
  He had ten thousand men;
He marched them up to the top of a hill,
  And he marched them down again.

And when they were up, they were up;
  And when they were down, they were
    down;
And when they were only half-way up,
  They were neither up nor down.

*Traditional*

2   *Rappetty-Tappetty*

Rappetty-tappetty, teetlety-tootlety,
Oh, what a wonderful noise!
Down the street with a teetlety-tootlety
Follow the girls and boys.
Teetlety-tootlety, teetlety-tootlety,
Teetlety-tootlety, toot!

*Clive Sansom*

# The Policeman

The noise that annoys
All the naughty little boys
Is the tramp of the feet
Of the policeman on his beat,
As he walks up and down
With a frown, with a frown,
As he walks up and down with a frown.

When he holds up his hand,
All the traffic has to stand.
Every car, every bus,
Has to stop without a fuss.
They must wait in a row
Till the policeman tells them, "Go!"
They must wait till the policeman tells
    them, "Go!"

And if anyone's about
Who shouldn't be about,
Then there isn't any doubt
He must very soon look out
For the tramp of the feet
Of the policeman on his beat,
For the tramp of his feet on the beat.

*Clive Sansom*

# The Engine Driver

The train goes running along the line,
   Jicketty-can, jicketty-can.
I wish it were mine, I wish it were mine,
   Jicketty-can, jicketty-can.
The engine driver stands in front—
   He makes it run, he makes it shunt.

     Out of the town,
     Out of the town,
     Over the hill,
     Over the down,
     Under the bridges,
     Across the lea,
     Over the ridges
     And down to the sea.

     With a jicketty-can, jicketty-can,
     Jicketty-jicketty-jicketty-can,
     Jicketty-can, jicketty-can . . .

*Clive Sansom*

# Sneezing

Sneeze on Monday, sneeze for danger;
Sneeze on Tuesday, meet a stranger;
Sneeze on Wednesday, sneeze for a letter;
Sneeze on Thursday, something better;
Sneeze on Friday, sneeze for sorrow—
Sneeze on Saturday, see your sweetheart
    tomorrow.

*Traditional*

# Tommy Tiddler

Little Tommy Tiddler
Is going to be a fiddler;
They've given him a fiddle,
And they've given him a bow.

Play, play, play, Tommy Tiddler!
Say, say, say, Tommy Tiddler!
Play a little twiddle
On the middle of your fiddle,
Or we'll go, we'll go, we'll go, go, go
And take away your fiddle and your bow.

*Paul Edmonds*

# Gobble and Hobble

The girl in the lane who couldn't speak
 plain
  Cried gobble, gobble, gobble.
The man on the hill who couldn't stand
 still
  Went hobble, hobble, hobble.


# The Whiteywash Man

Here's the whiteywash man!
White whiteywash—brown whiteywash—
Yellow whiteywash—green whiteywash!
Wash! Wash! I'm about!

*Negro street-cry, Philadelphia*


# Peter, Peter, Pumpkin-eater

Peter, Peter, pumpkin-eater,
Had a wife and couldn't keep her.
Put her in a pumpkin shell—
There he kept her very well!

# The Postman

Rat-a-tat-tat, Rat-a-tat-tat!
Rat-a-tat-tat, Tattoo!
That's the way the postman goes—
Rat-a-tat-tat, Tattoo!
Every morning at half-past eight
You hear a bang at the garden gate,
And Rat-a-tat-tat, Rat-a-tat-tat!
Rat-a-tat-tat, Tattoo!

*Clive Sansom*

# Billy Button

1   "Billy Button bought a buttered
        biscuit."
2   "Did Billy Button buy a buttered
        biscuit?"
3   "If Billy Button bought a buttered
        biscuit,
    Where's the buttered biscuit that
        Billy Button bought?"

# CRIES OF OLD LONDON

Thus go the cries in London Town:
First they go up street, and then they go down.

—*Thomas Heywood*, 1609

## Pear Seller

Pears for pies,
Come feast your eyes!
Ripest pears
Of every size.
    Who'll buy?
    Who'll buy?

## Tinker

Have you any work for a tinker, mistress?
Old brass, old pots, or kettles?
I'll mend them all with a tink, terry tink,
And never hurt your metals.

## Apple Seller

Here are fine golden pippins—
    Who'll buy them, who'll buy?
No one in London sells better than I—
    Who'll buy them, who'll buy?

# Nut Seller

Crack them and try them, before you buy
them,
Eight a penny, all new walnuts!
Crack them and try them, before you buy
them,
A shilling a hundred, all new walnuts!

# Cherry Seller

Round and sound,
Tuppence a pound,
Cherries! rare, ripe cherries!

As big as plums:
Who comes? who comes?
Cherries! rare, ripe cherries!

# Broom Seller

New brooms, maids, new brooms!
Buy my brooms
To sweep your rooms.
New brooms, maids, new brooms!

# The Grove

On the high road to Richmond,
    All in the Grove,
I heard a White Blackbird
    Sing for his love.
He sang so brightly,
He sang so lightly,
He sang so sprightly,
    All in the Grove!
Lilli-loo-loo-loo! lilli-loo-loo-loo!
    All down the Richmond Road—
Lilli-loo-loo-loo! lilli-loo-loo-loo!
    All in the Grove.

*Eleanor Farjeon*

# Jerry and James and John

There was an old woman who had three
    sons—
    Jerry and James and John.
Jerry was hanged, James was drowned,
John was lost and never was found;
And that was the end of all three sons—
    Jerry and James and John.

# Winds

In summer, winds blow softly;
They gently move the trees.
Only a few, green, outer leaves
Are stirring in the breeze:
     ffffssss

But later, when the autumn comes
And leaves are turning brown,
Winds, like an army, storm the wood
And tear its banners down:
     WH! . . . . . .

*Clive Sansom*

# The Blacksmith

A-hippity, hippity hop, heigh-ho!
Away to the blacksmith's shop we go.
    If you've a pony
    That's lost a shoe,
    You can get her another
    All shining and new—
A-hippity, hippity hop!

# Try

No hill too steep for Try to climb,
No ground too hard for Try to plough,
No field too wet for Try to drain,
No hole too big for Try to mend.

# The Fly

"There *is* a fly! I know there is!
I saw it on the wall.
But Clare and Barbara insist
There isn't one at all!"

# Five Plump Peas

Five plump peas in a pea-pod pressed,
One grew and two grew, and so did all
    the rest,
Grew and grew and grew and grew,
And grew and never stopped,
Till they grew so plump and portly
    That the pea-pod popped!

# Trotting

Clip-clop, clip-clop, clip-clop,
Hear the dog-cart trot down the lane—
Clip-clop to the town, and clop home again,
Clip-clop, clip-clop, clip-clop!

*Clive Sansom*


# Galloping

### 1

Gallop, grey mare, gallop,
Gallop through the glen.
Gallop up, and gallop down,
And gallop home again.

*Rodney Bennett*


### 2

Husky hi, husky hi,
Here comes Keery galloping by.
She carries her husband tied in a sack,
She carries him home on her horse's back.
Husky hi, husky hi,
Here comes Keery galloping by!

*Translated from the Norwegian by*
*Rose Fyleman*

# The Two Kings

There was a king met a king
    In a narrow lane.
Said this king to that king,
    "Where have you been?"

"Oh, I've been a-hunting
    The buck and the doe."
"Pray lend a dog to me
    That I may do so."

"Take the dog *Greedy Guts*."
    "What's the dog's name?"
"I've told you already."
    "Pray tell me again."

"GREEDY GUTS!"


# What the Sailor Saw

A sailor went to sea,
To see what he could see,
But the only thing the sailor saw
Was sea, sea, sea!

# The Muffin Man

Don't you know the muffin man,
　Don't you know his name?
Don't you know the muffin man
　That lives in our lane?
All around the Butter Cross,
　Up by St Giles's,
Up and down the Gullet shut,
　And call at Molly Miles's.

*Shropshire Folk-rhyme*


# Crosspatch, the Tailor

Crosspatch roams with a long black
　yardstick
　Out on the hills where the sun drops
　red,
Stuffing in the pockets of his green baize
　apron
　Thistledown for pillow-flock and
　gossamer for thread.

*Jonathan Field*

# Where are you going?

"Where are you going, big pig, big pig?"
"I'm going to dig in the garden."
"In the garden to dig! Disgraceful pig!"
"Beg pardon, ma'am, beg pardon."

*Mona Swann*

# Desperadoes

Without a thought for their own safety
    as they crept through the thick leaves,
They stormed the fortress and set free
    the three fat thieves.

# The Church Bells

Cling! Clang! Cling!
The bells begin to ring.
    Hear them chime
    As they tell the time:
Cling! Clang! Cling!

# Old Woman, Old Woman

"Old woman, old woman, will you come
    a-shearing?"
—"Speak a little louder, sir, I'm very
    hard of hearing."

"Old woman, old woman, will you come
    a-gleaning?"
—"Speak a little louder, sir, I cannot tell
    your meaning."

"Old woman, old woman, will you come
    a-walking?"
—"Speak a little louder, sir, or what's
    the use of talking."

"Old woman, old woman, shall I love
    you dearly?"
—"Thank you very kindly, sir—I hear
    you very clearly."

*Traditional*

# The Milkman

Clink, clink, clinketty-clink—
The milkman's on his rounds, I think.
Crunch, crunch, come the milkman's feet
Closer and closer along the street,
Then clink, clink, clinketty-clink—
He's left our bottles of milk to drink.

*Clive Sansom*


# The Dustman

Every Thursday morning,
Before you're quite awake,
Without the slightest warning
The house begins to shake
With a Biff! . . . Bàng!
Biff! Bang! Bàsh!

It's the dustman, who begins
(Bang! . . . Crash!)
To empty both the bins
Of their rubbish and their ash,
With a Biff! . . . Bàng!
Biff! Bang! Bàsh!

*Clive Sansom*

# Matthew Mears

There was a man who had a clock,
His name was Matthew Mears;
He wound it every single night
For five-and-twenty years.
But when that precious time-piece
    proved
An eight-day clock to be,
A madder man than Matthew Mears
You couldn't wish to see!

*Author unknown*

# Anthony Hay

Anthony Hay,
One holiday,
Thought he would go
For a swim in the bay,
A shark at play
Came that way—
Oh, what a shame!
Poor Anthony Hay!

*Peggy Noble*

# Kettledrums

*Drrr! . . . Drrr!*
*Drrr! . . . Drrr!*
Kettledrums are clearer,
Troops are coming nearer,
And the tread, tread, tread of their feet.
It's the never-ending rattle
Of the drummers' battle-prattle
As they all come marching down the
    street!
*Drrr . . . Drrr!*
*Drrr, Drrr, Drrr!*

*Clive Sansom*


# Walter Waddle

1  "Walter Waddle won a walking
    wager."
2  "Did Walter Waddle win a walking
    wager?"
3  "If Walter Waddle won a walking
    wager,
    Where's the walking wager that
        Walter Waddle won?"

# The Key of the King's Garden

I'll sell you the key of the king's garden;

I'll sell you the string that ties the key of
the king's garden;

I'll sell you the rat that gnawed the string
that ties the key of the king's garden;

I'll sell you the cat that caught the rat
that gnawed the string that ties the
key of the king's garden;

I'll sell you the dog that bit the cat that
caught the rat that gnawed the string
that ties the key of the king's garden.

# Counting-out Rhyme

Vizzery, vazzery, vozery vem,
Tizzery, tazzery, tozery tem,
Hiram, Jiram, cockrem, spirem,
Poplar, rollin, gem.

*Warwickshire Folk-rhyme*

# HOME-MADE RHYMES

*Interesting rhymes might be made up around the following ideas and sounds :*

| | |
|---|---|
| Motorboat engine | pt pt pt pt pt |
| Water dripping from tap or medicine poured from bottle | p . . . p . . . p . . .<br>*( Lightly, with loose lips )* |
| Mosquito | zzzz zzzz zzzz |
| Garden sprinkler | s-sh . . . s-sh . . . |
| Fire-hose | zh (as in pleasure)<br>*( varied strengths )* |
| Horse neighing | bwwwww<br>*( vibrating loose lips )* |
| Horses' hooves | t-t, t-t, t-t<br>*( walk, trot, gallop )* |

| | |
|---|---|
| Steam escaping | sh<br>*(varied strengths)* |
| Kettle hissing | sssssssss |
| Telephone | br-br . . . br-br |
| Steam-train starting,<br>gathering speed | ch------ch------ch<br>*(Changing pace<br>and energy)* |
| Humming top | mmmmmmmmm<br>*(on different<br>pitches)* |
| Aeroplane diving | nnnnnn<br>*(with pitch<br>changes)* |
| Vacuum cleaner | th (as in 'those') |
| Electric shaver | vvvvvvvvv |

## PART 3

# You Can Take a Tub

You can take a tub with a rub and a
     scrub
In a two-foot tank of tin,
Or stand and look at the whirling brook
And think about jumping in;
You can chatter and shake by the cold,
     black lake—
But the kind of bath for me
Is to take a dip from the side of a ship
In the trough of the rolling sea.

You may lie and dream in the bed of a
     stream
When an August day is dawning.
Or believe it's nice to break the ice
On your tub of a winter's morning;
You may sit and shiver beside the river—
But the kind of bath for me
Is to take a dip from the side of a ship
In the trough of the rolling sea.

*Edward Parry*

# Yawning Paul

To see Paul yawning
    Is a sight.
He yawns and yawns
    With all his might.
He yawns all night
    And day and all.
That's why we call him
    Yawning Paul.

*Rodney Bennett*


# Peckham Rye

"Who'll buy our Rye?
    Who'll buy? who'll buy?"—
The pretty girls of Peckham cry.
"The ears are full as they can hold
And heavy as a purse of gold.
Sweeter corn you will not find
For the London mills to grind—
    Come buy, come buy
    Our Peckham Rye!"

*Eleanor Farjeon*

# As I Walked by Myself

As I walked by myself,
And talked to myself,
   Myself said unto me,
"Look to thyself,
Take care of thyself,
   For nobody cares for thee."

I answered myself,
And said to myself,
   In the self-same repartee,
"Look to thyself,
Or *not* look to thyself,
   The self-same thing will be."

# Gaffer Gilpin

1  "Gaffer Gilpin got a goose and gander."
2  "Did Gaffer Gilpin get a goose and
        gander?"
3  "If Gaffer Gilpin got a goose and
        gander,
   Where are the goose and gander that
        Gaffer Gilpin got?"

# Clocks and Watches

Our great
Steeple clock
Goes TICK——TOCK
TICK——TOCK;

Our small
Mantel clock
Goes TICK-TACK, TICK-TACK,
TICK-TACK, TICK-TACK;

Our little
Pocket watch
Goes *tick-a-tacker, tick-a-tacker,*
*tick-a-tacker, tick.*

# The Lazy Lizard

I'm a lazy old lizard
    Who lives at the zoo,
And catches the flies,
    And swallows them, too.

*Mona Swann*

# The Band in the Park

Hark, hark, hark!
Hark, hark, hark!
Listen to the band in the park!
With its "hum hum hum,"
And its "rumpty tumpty tum,"
The cymbals going "clang"
And the drums going "bang,"
As they play, play, play, play, play,
play, play,
As they play, play, play, in the middle
of the day,
As they play, play, play in the park.

*Paul Edmonds*


# Under the Trees

"Under the trees!"—Who but agrees
That there is magic in words such as
these?
Promptly one sees shake in the breeze
Stately lime avenues haunted of bees.

*C. S. Calverley*

# Purring

*Prrr!*
*Prrr!*
Our old cat
Snores like that,
Snoozing in her old armchair.
She smoothes her coat
And warbles in her throat:
*Prrrrrrrrrrr!*


# Conversation

"Are you off to school, sir?"
—"No, sir."
        —"Why, sir?"
—"Because I have a cold, sir."
—"Where did you get the cold, sir?"
—"Up at the North Pole, sir."
—"What were you doing there, sir?"
—"Catching a Polar bear, sir."
—"How many did you see, sir?"
—"One, two, three, sir!"

*Irish rhyme*

# What's the Weather?

Whether the weather be fine,
Or whether the weather be not,
Whether the weather be cold,
Or whether the weather be hot—
We'll weather the weather,
Whatever the weather,
Whether we like it or not.

*Traditional*

# Christmas Pudding

Take milk, eggs, and raisins.
Take milk, eggs, and raisins; suet and
    sugar and flour.
Take milk, eggs, and raisins; suet and
    sugar and flour; candied-peel
    and breadcrumbs.
Take milk, eggs, and raisins; suet and
    sugar and flour; candied-peel
    and breadcrumbs—and boil
    for eight hours.

# The Shop Bell

The bell-spring swings
And the small bell rings
With a tingaling, tingaling,
Tingalinga ling.
"Here's someone who is willing
To spend a silver shilling,
So come along,
Dingadong!
Tingalinga ling!"

*Rodney Bennett*


# Paddy's Breeches

Paddy O'Flynn
Had no breeches to wear,
So they bought him a sheepskin
And made him a pair.
With the woolly side out
And the skinny side in,
It made some good breeches
For Paddy O'Flynn.

*Irish rhyme*

# Butterflies

All day long in the garden
Are butterflies flitting by,
White, pale yellow, and orange bright
And some like the blue of the sky.

# The Angler

To a little nook by the side of a brook
I took a big pole and a funny black
       hook.
I stood and I stood as long as I could—
Then the nook by the brook I forsook.

*Audrey Heine*

# A Peanut

A peanut sat on the railroad track,
His heart was all a-flutter.
Along came a train, the 10.15—
*Toot-toot!*—peanut butter!

*American rhyme*

# The Dream of a Girl at Sevenoaks

Seven sweet singing-birds up in a tree;
Seven swift sailing-ships white upon the
sea;
Seven bright weather-cocks shining in
the sun;
Seven slim race-horses ready for the run;
Seven gold butterflies flitting overhead;
Seven red roses in a garden bed;
Seven white lilies with honey-bees inside
them;
And seven round rainbows with clouds
to divide them . . .

Seven nights running I dreamed it all
plain—
With bread and jam for supper, I could
dream it all again.

*Author unknown*

# Clunton and Clunbury

Clunton and Clunbury,
Clungunford and Clun,
Are the quietest places
Under the sun.

*Shropshire Folk-rhyme*

# Pimlico

Pimlico, pamlico, pumpkins and peas!
Pepper them properly, else you will sneeze.
Pop in a pipkin and leave them till one,
Pimlico, pamlico, then they'll be done!

*Eleanor Farjeon*

# The Drawing

In India or Pakistan
I saw an artist draw a pear.
I'm *sure* I saw him drawing there—
Or was it China or Japan?

# The Roundabout

Round and round the roundabout,
Down the "slippery stair"—
I'm always to be found about
When circus men are there.
The music of the roundabout,
The voices in the air,
The horses as they pound about,
The boys who shout and stare—
There's such a lovely sound about
A circus or a fair.

*Clive Sansom*

# Windy Nights

Rumbling in the chimneys,
    Rattling at the doors,
Round the roofs and round the roads
    The rude wind roars;
Raging through the darkness,
    Raving through the trees,
Racing off again across
    The great grey seas.

*Rodney Bennett*

## The Watchman's Cry

Give, care to your clocks!
Beware your locks,
Your fire and your light!
And God give you good-night!
   Past nine o'clock!
     *(Going away in the distance)*
     Past nine o'clock!


## Granfer Grig

   Granfer Grig
   Had a pig
In a field of clover.
   The pig he died,
   Granfer cried,
And all the fun was over.

*Cornish Folk-rhyme*


## Where do you come from?

The north for greatness,
The east for health,
The south for neatness,
The west for wealth.

# Song of the Duchess

Speak roughly to your little boy,
    And beat him when he sneezes:
He only does it to annoy,
    Because he knows it teases.

*Chorus:*
wow! wow! wow!

I speak severely to my boy,
    I beat him when he sneezes;
For he can thoroughly enjoy
    The pepper when he pleases.

*Chorus:*
wow! wow! wow!

*Lewis Carroll*

# A Catch Rhyme

Round and round the rugged rock
    The ragged rascal ran.
Say how many Rs in *that*
    And you're a clever man.

# Old Farmer Giles

Old Farmer Giles
He walked five miles
With his fine sheepdog, Rover.

Old Farmer Giles
When he came to the stiles,
He "upped" and jumped right over!

# Penelope's Pearls

Pearls please pretty Penelope,
    pretty Penelope, pretty Penelope;
Pearls please pretty Penelope,
    pretty Penelope Pring.
I would like to bring pearls for Penelope,
    pearls for Penelope, pretty Penelope,
I would like to bring pearls for Penelope,
    pretty Penelope Pring.

*Rodney Bennett*

# Tracking

We're òn the vìllain's tráck . . .
We're on the villain's track . . .
We're . . . on . . . the trail . . .
Of Tarry — Trouser — Jack . . .
*(Repeat)*

# Marching Rhymes

### I

The Emperor Napoleon has a hundred
　　thousand men,
The Emperor Napoleon has a hundred
　　thousand men,
The Emperor Napoleon has a hundred
　　thousand men,
　As we go marching along.

### 2

We be the King's men, hale and hearty,
Marching to meet one Buonaparty;
If he won't sail, lest the wind should blow,
We shall have marched for nothing, O!

*From "The Dynasts" by Thomas Hardy*

## My Grandmother

My grandmother sent me a new-fashioned
three-cornered cambric country-cut
handkerchief.
Not an old-fashioned three-cornered
cambric country-cut handkerchief,
but a new-fashioned three-cornered
cambric country-cut handkerchief.

## Peter Piper

Peter Piper picked a peck of pickled
pepper;
A peck of pickled pepper Peter Piper
picked.
If Peter Piper picked a peck of pickled
pepper,
Where's the peck of pickled pepper
Peter Piper picked?

# Swan Swam over the Sea

Swan swam over the sea—
　Swim, swan, swim!
Swan swam back again—
　Well swum, swan!

# Two Fellows

Once a fellow met a fellow
In a field of beans.
Said a fellow to a fellow,
"If a fellow asks a fellow,
Can a fellow tell a fellow
What a fellow means?"

# The Fly and the Flea

A fly and a flea in a flue
Were wondering what they should do.
Said the fly, "Let us flee!"
Said the flea, "Let us fly!"
So they flew through a flaw in the flue!

# Betty's Butter

Betty bought a bit of butter,
Said: "~~My bit of~~ butter's bitter.
If I put it in my batter,
It will make my batter bitter.
Better buy some fresher butter."
Betty's mother said she'd let her,
So she bought some better butter,
And it made her batter better.

# The Kettle

There's a little metal kettle
That is sitting near the settle.
You will hear the tittle-tattle
Of the lid begin to rattle
When the kettle starts to boil.
What a pretty prittle-prattle
Of the kettle near the settle,
Such a merry tittle-tattle
When the lid begins to rattle
And the kettle starts to boil.

*Gwynneth Thurburn*

# The Peanut Seller

Peanuts!
Two bags for five!

They brush your teeth,
They curl your hair;
They make you feel
Like a millionaire!

Peanuts!
Two bags for five!

*Street-cry from New Orleans*


# Snoring at Sea

On deck beneath the awning,
I dozing lay and yawning;
It was the grey of dawning,
  Ere yet the sun arose.

And above the funnel's roaring,
And the fitful wind's deploring,
I heard the cabin snoring
  With universal nose.

*William M. Thackeray*

# Questions

Which and where and why and when
Are words I keep saying again and again.
Over and over without any hitch—
When and where and why and which.
Whatever the answer, I always declare
Which and why and when and where.
Whatever the answer, I always reply,
Where? and when? and which? and why?

*Peggy Noble*


# Lightships

All night long when the wind is high,
    NnnnnnNnnnnnNnnnnn,
The lightships moan and moan to the sky,
    NnnnnnNnnnnnNnnnnn.
Their foghorns whine when the mist runs
      free,
    NnnnnnNnnnnnNnnnnn,
Warning the men on the ships at sea,
    NnnnnnNnnnnnNnnnnn.

*Clive Sansom*

# Nonsense

So she went into the garden to cut a
    cabbage to make an apple-pie.
Just then a great she-bear, coming
    down the street, poked its nose
    into the shop-window.
"What! No soap?"
So he died, and she very imprudently
    married the barber.
And there were present at the wedding
    the Joblillies, and the Piccannies,
    and the Garyulies—
And the Great Panjandrum himself,
    with the little round button on
    top!
So they fell to playing Catch-as-catch-
    can, till the gunpowder ran out
    at the heels of their boots.

*Samuel Foote*

# So Tired

"Oh dear, oh dear! I woke at dawn
　　　this morning
To hear Paul calling over the garden
　　　wall:
'Come on, George! It's time to stop your
　　　snoring.
Crawl out of bed and play us a game
　　　of ball!'

I've caught and caught that wretched
　　　ball all morning—
Worn myself out, hurling it across the
　　　lawn.
And now my jaw is falling without
　　　warning:
If I'm not . . . careful, I'll . . . begin to
　　　. . . YAWN."
　　　*(He does!)*

*Clive Sansom*

# Timbuktoo

Oh, I want to go to Timbuktoo,
  Woolla-woolla woolla-woolla way;
Where the girls are black, and the boys
      are, too,
  Woolla-woolla, woolla-woolla way.

It's there you see the chimpanzee
Swinging from the branch of a great
      big tree.
It's there you hear the big baboon
Singing in the night the monkey tune:
  Woolla-woolla way,
  Woolla-woolla way,
  Woolla-woolla, woolla-woolla way.

*Paul Edmonds*

# The Legacy

My father left me just all he was able—
One bowl, one bottle, one label,
Two bowls, two bottles, two labels,
Three bowls, three bottles, three labels,
Four bowls, four bottles, four labels . . .

# No Answer

There was an old man who said "Well!
Will nobody answer this bell?
   I have pulled day and night
   Till my hair has grown white,
But *nobody* answers the bell!"

*Edward Lear*

# The Cheerful Crocodile

Upon the sacred river Nile
There lives a lazy long reptile
Who's full of greed and full of guile,
Whose skin's as rough as any file,
Who's got a wide deceptive smile
That's visible for half a mile . . .
Of course you've guessed that all the while
I'm speaking of the crocodile.
Perhaps you don't admire his style—
His manners, I admit, are vile,
But glum folk—those who never smile—
Might with advantage pause awhile
And ponder on the crocodile.

*Thomas Bolt*

# Baby's Drinking Song

for a baby learning for the first
time to drink from a cup

*(Vivace)*

Sip a little
Sup a little
From your little
Cup a little
Sup a little
Sip a little
Put it to your
Lip a little
Tip a little
Tap a little
Not into your
Lap or it'll
Drip a little
Drop a little
On the table
Top a little.

*James Kirkup*

# Galloping Rhymes

### I

Trample! trample! went the roan,
   Trap! trap! went the grey;
But pad! pad! pad! like a thing that
    was mad
   My chestnut broke away . . .

*Walter Thornbury*

### 2

*Tlot-tlot, tlot-tlot!* Had they heard it?
   The horse-hoofs ringing clear;
*Tlot-tlot, tlot-tlot,* in the distance? Were
   they deaf that they did not hear?

*Alfred Noyes*

### 3

Galloping, galloping, galloping steed;
Six reins slackened and dull with sweat,
Galloping, galloping, still we speed,
Galloping, galloping, galloping yet.

Galloping, galloping, galloping steed;
Six reins, silken reins, start and strain.
Galloping, galloping, still we speed.
News—what news—from the king's
   domain?

*From the Chinese*

### 4

We are they who come faster than fate:
We are they who ride early or late,
We storm at your ivory gate—
Pale kings of the sunset, beware!

*J. E. Flecker*

### 5

Come, fill up my cup; come, fill up my can!
Come, saddle my horses and call up my
    men!
Come, open the West Gate and let us go
    free,
For it's up with the bonnets of Bonnie
    Dundee!

### 6

I sprang to the stirrup, and Joris, and he;
I galloped, Dirck galloped, we galloped
    all three;
"Good speed!" cried the watch★, as the
    gate-bolts undrew;
"Speed!" echoed the wall to us galloping
    through;
Behind shut the postern†, the lights sank
    to rest,
And into the midnight we galloped abreast.

★Watchman                       *Robert Browning*
†City gate

# The Dark Wood

In the dark, dark wood, there was a dark,
    dark house,
And in that dark, dark house, there was
    a dark, dark room.
And in that dark, dark room, there was
    a dark, dark cupboard,
And in that dark, dark cupboard, there
    was a dark, dark shelf.
And on that dark, dark shelf, there was
    a dark, dark box,
And in that dark, dark box, there was a
    GHOST!

# Greasy Ghosts

There were three ghosts,
Sitting on posts,
Eating buttered toasts,
And greasing their fists
Right up to their wrists—
Weren't they beasts!

# Scythe Song

Mowers, weary and brown and blithe,
    What is the word methinks ye know—
Endless over-word that the scythe
    Sings to the blades of the grass below?
Scythes that swing in the grass and
       clover,
    Something, still, they say as they pass;
What is the word that, over and over,
    Sings the scythe to the flowers and
       grass?

*Hush, ah, hush!* the scythes are saying,
    *Hush and heed not,* and fall asleep;
*Hush,* they say to the grasses swaying,
    *Hush,* they sing to the clover deep.
*Hush*—'tis the lullaby Time is
       singing—
    *Hush,* and heed not, for all things
       pass,
*Hush, ah, hush!* and the scythes are
       swinging
    Over the clover, over the grass.

*Andrew Lang*

# Harvest-home Cry

A knack, a knack!
Well cut, well bound!
Well reaped, well stacked!
Well saved from the ground!
Whoop! Hurray!

*Devonshire Folk-rhyme*

# The Centipede

The centipede was happy quite,
Until the toad in fun
Said, "Pray which leg goes after which?"
Which worked his mind to such a pitch
He lay distracted in a ditch
Considering *how* to run.

*Mrs Edward Craster*

# Rowing

Row, boatman, row!
Row, boatman, row!
Over the foam and far from home,
Row, boatman, row!

# Play

Play, play, while as yet it is day—
While the sweet sunlight is warm on the
      brae★
Hark to the lark singing lay upon lay,
While the brown squirrel eats nuts on
      the spray
And in the apple-leaves chatters the jay.
Play, play, even as they!

What though the cowslips ye pluck will
      decay?
What though the grass will be presently
      hay?
What though the noise that ye make
      should dismay
Old Mrs Clutterbuck over the way?
Play, play, for your locks will grow
      grey—
Even the marbles ye sport with are clay!

*C. S. Calverley*

★A steep bank

# Three Thirsty Men

The first three men felt thirsty
    after throwing the ball so far.
So they followed the throng through the
    fairground and freshened their
    throats at the bar.

# The Pensive Oyster

"What noise annoys the pensive oyster,
Brooding in his shady cloister?"

"The wild halloo of noisy boys
The pensive oyster most annoys."

*Jonathan Field*

# Doctor Fell

I do not love thee, Doctor Fell.
The reason why I cannot tell;
But this I know, and know full well—
I do not love thee, Doctor Fell.

*Thomas Brown*

# The Early Bird

Poor Mr Worm!—he does not see
The Early Bird upon the tree.
But with unswerving eye and grim
The Early Bird's observing him.

A worm may turn, some persons state—
If this one's turned, he's turned too late.
Before he can as much as *squirm*,
The Early Bird has caught the worm.

Gone are the joys of terrafirma!
Down he goes without a murmur—
While, from his perch, the Early Bird
Chirps as if nothing had occurred.

*Clive Sansom*

# Oh!

He gave a groan
And then a moan
Because he bumped
His funny bone!

*Peggy Noble*

# The Sickening Disillusionment of Don José, Picador

Don José was a Picador,
    A man of many parts.
One day he tried to kick a door
    By angry fits and starts.
He thought it was a wicker door,
    Like those they have in France.
But when the silly Picador
Found out it was a thicker door,
A sad expression flickered o'er
    His vapid countenance.

*Ralph Wotherspoon*

# Hamish's Hammer

"How on earth does Hamish Hamilton
    hurl such a heavy hammer?"
—"He stands with his feet apart, and
    his huge hands held together;
Then, after heaving it high and hurriedly
    around his head,
With a twirl of his kilt he sends it hurtling
    across the heather."

*Clive Sansom*

# Hauling the Bowline*

Haul on the bowline,
The fore and maintop bowline,
Haul on the bowline,
The bowline HAUL.

Haul upon the bowline,
So early in the morning,
Haul upon the bowline,
The bowline HAUL.

Haul on the bowline,
The bonny ship's a-sailing,
Haul on the bowline,
The bowline HAUL.

Haul upon the bowline,
It's a far cry to pay-day,
Haul upon the bowline,
The bowline HAUL.

*Sea Chanty*

*Pronounced *bohlin*

# Listen to the Band

Listen! Listen!
Listen to the band!

Drums drumming,
Banjos strumming—
We're all coming
To listen to the band!

Fiddles twanging,
Cymbals clanging,
Bass drums banging—
Listen to the band!

Sopranos whining,
Tenors pining—
All combining
To try and drown the band!

Listen! Listen!
Listen to the band!

*Clive Sansom*

# Polynesian Picnic

There were plump Polynesians, so
　　travellers say,
Who were usually thought to be casual
　　and gay;
They treasured their leisure with
　　measureless pleasure,
And needed no persuasion to laze all
　　the day.

But any intrusion upon their seclusion
Would end in conclusions so final, that
　　soon
Each painful intrusion appeared but
　　illusion
Where plump Polynesians caroused with
　　the moon.

*Mona Swann*

# Algy No More

Algy met a bear,
The bear met Algy,
The bear grew bulgy—
The bulge was Algy.

## Night-lights

There is no need to light a night-light
On a light night like tonight;
For a night-light's light's a slight light
When the moonlight's white and bright.

## Grey Geese

Three grey geese in a green field grazing:
In a green field grazing are three grey geese.
The grey geese graze while I am gazing:
I gaze and gaze till the grey geese cease.

## Shutting the Shutter

A woman to her boy did utter:
"Go, my son, and shut the shutter."
—"The shutter's shut," the boy did mutter,
"I cannot shut it any shutter."

## Washing Instructions

"Wash your face and hands, my boy,"
        his Uncle Will insists,
"But mind you watch your wrist-watch
        when you wash and rinse your wrists."

# HOW TO USE THE RHYMES

Most of the technical aspects of speech are covered by these rhymes:

    Breath control: controlling quantity and force of breath
    Resonance and forward production
    Projection: speaking out without shouting
    Vigour and agility in the use of tongue and lips
    Pronunciation: formation of consonants and vowels
    Phrasing: linking of words into sense-groups
    Stressing and emphasis: for clarity of meaning
    Variety of tone: expressing mood and feeling
    Range of pitch and tune
    Rhythm
    Changes in pace and volume

The rhymes are offered with the following suggestions:

1 They are rhymes for speech practice, not poems for appreciation.

2 Although arranged in three sections according to suggested age groupings, much depends on children's previous experience.

3 The best way of introducing a rhyme is to say it to the class. Unless the rhyme is a short one, it is advisable to avoid whole-class repetition, which can be either too heavy or too jingly. Group work, individual speaking or sequence-speaking are preferable, according to the content and form of the rhyme. Writing on the blackboard should generally be avoided.

4 Essentials are enjoyment, individuality, liveliness, clarity. These are most likely to be found if a child identifies himself with the people in the rhymes and their actions. There is usually more than one 'right' way of saying a rhyme. Children should be given every chance of discovering their own interpretation.

5 Although the children should be allowed to enjoy the rhyme for its own sake and need not be conscious of its technical purpose, the teacher *does* need to remember the purpose (see the notes on individual rhymes which follow) and should aim at achieving it, though not through exaggeration. The best interpretation, even of a tongue twister, is one that sounds natural and effortless.

6 Practice in individual sounds is not the main purpose of these rhymes and teachers are advised to concentrate on the more general aspects of voice and speech. However, a speech-sound may sometimes require separate attention. When this is necessary, care should be taken that the sound does not assume too great an importance and falls easily into the main pattern of the line.

7 Care should be given to *rhythm*.* It is important, however, not to confuse this with *metre*: flow and flexibility are essential. Over-stressing is to be avoided.

8 The teacher also needs to be aware of the place of the 'neutral vowel' in normal English. Examples of this indefinite sound are the first syllable of 'above' and the last syllable of 'China'. It occurs in many relatively unimportant words such as 'a', 'the', 'of' etc. when used in a spoken phrase. We must be sure to keep this pronunciation and not say 'ay', 'thee', 'ov' under the mistaken impression that we are improving speech and making clear communication easier. The same applies to such words as 'dustman', 'spoken', 'sailor'.

9 Over-precise speech is as bad as slovenly speech in impeding the expression of ideas and feelings. In word-groups such as 'bad dog' and 'last time', for example, we usually double the length of the repeated consonant by delaying its explosion; we do not make two separated sounds. Also, the final consonant of a word, though it needs to be distinct, is not as strong as an initial consonant.

10 Certain rhymes give practice in that tricky consonant-group *tl* ('little'). It needs to be considered as one sound rather than two: the *l* is formed while the tongue still holds the *t* position. So the normal pronunciation is *li-tl*, not *li-tul*. The same is true of the *dl* group ('middle'). Similarly, 'button' is *bu-tn*, not *bu-ton*.

11 Finally, speech technique must never become an end in itself. Rhymes and exercises should be part only of a comprehensive programme of speech education,† covering children's conversation during shared activities, individual talks, small-group discussions, free but disciplined drama, and the speaking of prose and verse. Our aim is not so much to produce 'nice' speech as effective users of speech.

*Rhythm Rhymes* by Ruth Sansom (Black) gives additional help in rhythmic appreciation by linking words and movement.

†*Speech and Communication in the Primary School* by Clive Sansom (Black) outlines such a course.

# PART 1

## PART 2

## PART 3

first stanza should occupy the same space of time as 'Tick-a-tacker, tick-a-tacker, tick-a-tacker, tick' in the third stanza.

77 THE LAZY LIZARD Tongue action. Consonants *l, z*.

78 THE BAND IN THE PARK Firm, lively attack. Diphthong *ay*.

78 UNDER THE TREES Vowel *ee*.

79 PURRING Lightness, tongue agility.

79 CONVERSATION Range and variety.

80 WHAT'S THE WEATHER? Agility. In most parts of England there is no difference between the pronunciation of 'whether' and 'weather'. The *wh* sound should not be insisted upon where it is not normally used.

80 CHRISTMAS PUDDING Breath control, adjusting to length of phrases. Each paragraph should be on a single breath.

81 THE SHOP BELL Consonant *ng*. Light, agile speech.

81 PADDY'S BREECHES Agility and variety. 'Breeches' is pronounced 'britchiz'.

82 BUTTERFLIES Lightness. Diphthong I (high).

82 THE ANGLER Vowel *u* (cook).

82 A PEANUT Tongue twister.

83 THE DREAM OF A GIRL AT SEVENOAKS Lightness. Variation of tone and volume. Consonant *s*: clarity without hissing.

84 CLUNTON AND CLUNBURY Lightness. Vowel *u* (but). Local rhyme quoted by A. E. Housman in *A Shropshire Lad*. The villages are named after the river Colonne or Clone.

84 PIMLICO Forward production. Consonant *p*. One of a series of rhymes on London place names. A pipkin is a small earthenware dish.

84 THE DRAWING Avoidance of intrusive *r* where no *r* occurs in the spelling (Indiar or).

85 THE ROUNDABOUT Diphthong *ow*. Range and continuity.

85 WINDY NIGHTS Consonant *r*. 'Atmosphere'.

86 THE WATCHMAN'S CRY Speaking out without shouting.

86 GRANFER GRIG Variety.

86 WHERE DO YOU COME FROM? Consonant *th*.

87 SONG OF THE DUCHESS Range of pitch. Variation in loudness.

87 A CATCH RHYME Consonant *r*. The catch is that there is no 'r' in "that".

88 OLD FARMER GILES Diphthong I (high).

88 PENELOPE'S PEARLS Lip agility.

89 TRACKING Slow, stealthy rhythm. Note pause at end of the line: there are four stresses to each line, but the last one is silent.

89 THE EMPEROR NAPOLEON Marching rhythm.

89 WE BE THE KING'S MEN Brisk, lively rhythm.

90  MY GRANDMOTHER Tongue twister – and brain twister! Shift of emphasis. This rhyme and the next two are printed in Dr Wallis's *Grammatica Lingua Anglicana*, 1674, as being "certain cures for the hiccup if repeated in one breath".

90  PETER PIPER Tongue twister, encouraging lip agility.

91  SWAN SWAM OVER THE SEA Play on vowels *a, u, i*.

91  TWO FELLOWS General agility.

91  THE FLY AND THE FLEA Play on vowels *ee, oo, I*.

92  BETTY'S BUTTER Play on vowels *a, u, i, e*. Consonant *t*.

92  THE KETTLE Tongue twister, encouraging forward production and tongue agility. Consonant-group *tl*.

93  THE PEANUT SELLER Projection. One of the Southern Street Cries of the USA collected by Mrs Curren Hamm. "Two bags for five" means two bags for five cents.

93  SNORING AT SEA Vowel *aw*, consonant *ng*.

94  QUESTIONS Consonant *wh*. The pronunciation 'hwich', 'hwen' should not be insisted on where the pronunciations 'wich' and 'wen' are more normal.

94  LIGHTSHIPS Nasal resonance. Projection. "Nnnnnn-NnnnnnNnnnnn" to be said on a single breath, but with the energy renewed at each capital N.

95  NONSENSE Range and variety in tone and pitch. Charles Macklin, the actor, boasted that he could repeat anything by heart after once reading it. Samuel Foote, who heard him, composed this passage as a test.

96  SO TIRED Oral resonance, lower jaw. Vowel *aw*.

97  TIMBUKTOO Vigour and agility.

97  THE LEGACY Breath control. Consonant-groups *bl, tl*. How many lines can be said on one breath without effort?

98  NO ANSWER Variety. The old man may be angry, indignant, pathetic, or merely stating a fact.

98  THE CHEERFUL CROCODILE Phrasing. Diphthong I (high).

99  BABY'S DRINKING SONG Forward production. Agility. The author suggests that it may be read three times in succession, getting faster and faster each time.

100  TRAMPLE! TRAMPLE! WENT THE ROAN Rhythm. Change in volume.

100  TLOT-TLOT, TLOT-TLOT! Rhythm. Vigour and agility.

100  GALLOPING, GALLOPING, GALLOPING STEED Breath control. Pace and rhythm.

101  WE ARE THEY WHO COME FASTER THAN FATE Rhythm. Pace.

101  COME, FILL UP MY CUP Rhythm. Compare with other galloping rhymes.

101  I SPRANG TO-THE STIRRUP Firm, quick articulation without losing the sense of the story.

# ACKNOWLEDGEMENTS

Grateful acknowledgement is made to the following copyright holders for additional rhymes included in this revised edition:

Evelyn Abraham for "The Busy Bee", "The Cow Says" and "Haircut".

Mrs Joan Bennett for "Penelope's Pearls" by Rodney Bennett.

The Executors of the late Christopher Chamberlain for his poem "The Foolish Man".

The Clarendon Press, Oxford, for "The Dark Wood" from *The Lore and Language of School Children* by Iona and Peter Opie.

James Kirkup for "Baby's Drinking Song".

Macmillan, London and Basingstoke, for "Lily Lee" and "Woodpecker" by Isobel Best from *Speech Training in the Primary School.*

Pitman Publishing, London, for part of "Timbuktoo" by Paul Edwards from *Rhythmic Tunes and Songs for Children* and for "The Kettle" by Gwynneth Thurburn from *New Speech.*

Shirley K. Vickery for "Mice".

The following also kindly gave their permission to include rhymes in the original selection:

Margaret Barnard for "Look Out!", "If I had plenty of money", "Rain", "Tommy Tiddler" and "The Band in the Park" by Paul Edmonds from *Rhymes for Children* (Pitman).

Rodney Bennett and Evans Brothers for "Hoppety's House", "Bottles of Water" and "Gallop, Grey Mare" from *First Steps in Speech Training;* and for "Sheep and Lambs", "The Shop Bell", "Windy Nights" and "Yawning Paul" from *The Playway of Speech Training.*

Thomas Bolt for an extract from "The Cheerful Crocodile" from Guy Pertwee's *Reciter's Second Treasury* (Routledge).

Caryl Brahms and Victor Gollancz Ltd for part of "The King's High Drummer" from *The Moon on my Left.*

Walter de la Mare and Faber & Faber Ltd for "The Huntsmen" from *Peacock Pie.*

Eleanor Farjeon and Gerald Duckworth Ltd for "The Grove", "Pimlico" and "Peckham Rye" from *Nursery Rhymes of London Town.*

Rose Fyleman and The Society of Authors for "Singing Time" from *The Fairy Green* (Methuen); and for "Bibblibonty" and "Husky Hi" from *Widdy-Widdy-Wurkey* (Blackwell).

Robert Graves and A. P. Watt & Co for "I Have a Little Cough" from *The Less Familiar Nursery Rhymes* (Benn).

Agnes Curren Hamm and The Tower Press, Milwauki, for "Toys", "Listening" and "The Peanut Seller" from *Choral*

*Speaking Technique;* and Audrey Heine for "The Angler" from the same book.

The Trustees of the Hardy Estate and Macmillan, London and Basingstoke, for lines from *The Dynasts* by Thomas Hardy.

Macmillan, London and Basingstoke, for "Motoring", "Silly Billy", "Threads and Thimbles", "The Clock", "Where are you going?", "The Lazy Lizard" and "Polynesian Picnic" by Mona Swann from *Trippingly on the Tongue.*

J. E. Mulliner for "Dandelion Clocks".

Sir Edward Parry for "You Can Take a Tub" from *Kata-wampus.*

Irene Pawsey for "Goose Girl".

Ralph Wotherspoon and *The Cherwell* for "The Sickening Disillusionment of Don José, Picador".

Jonathan Field, Ruth Large, Peggy Noble and Winifred Kingdon-Ward for original rhymes first published in *Speech Rhymes.*

It is impossible to give the source of all the rhymes in this book. Some were jotted down while the editor was searching for material for class lessons. Others came from an oral tradition belonging to our village communities. Apologies are offered to any author or copyright holder whose rights have been unintentionally infringed and due acknowledgement will be made in subsequent editions on notification being made to the publishers.

# INDEX OF FIRST LINES